Scholastic Transition Program

Student Workbook

LEVEL A

Illustration Credits

Randy Verougstraete pages 4, 5, 6, 7, 11, 12
Bart Rivers pages 15, 16, 19, 21, 22,
74, 76, 80, 81
Hatley Mason pages 24, 26, 27, 29, 30, 32
Cover art: © Maya Brooks

Abbey Carter pages 35, 36, 39, 40, 41, 42
Susanne DeMarco pages 44, 45, 46, 50, 51, 52
Slug Signorino pages 54, 55, 56, 60, 61, 62,
Ruth Linstromberg pages 65, 66, 70, 71, 72
Tint art by Vincent Jeffrey

Copyright © 1998 Scholastic Inc. All rights reserved.
Published by Scholastic Inc.
Printed in the U.S.A.
ISBN 0-590-11576-6

2 3 4 5 6 7 8 9 10   34   03 02 01 00 99 98

Table of Contents

Name _____   Date _____

Life on a Ranch

Story Words

fox a wild animal with red-brown fur

chicken a bird raised for its meat and eggs

ranch a large area of land for raising animals

wax a material used to make candles

coyote a wild animal that looks like a dog

Everyday Words

fence something that protects an area

hole an opening in something

night the time when it is dark outside

man an adult male human being

hill an area of high land, smaller than a mountain

 A Draw a line from each word to its meaning.

1. chicken   a. a place to raise animals

2. wax   b. a wild doglike animal

3. ranch   c. material used to make candles

4. fox   d. a wild animal with red-brown fur

5. coyote   e. a bird

 B Put a check by the correct answer.

1. **When is it night?**   __ when it's dark outside   __ when the sun is out

2. **What is a man?**   __ a teenager   __ an adult male

3. **What goes around a ranch and protects it?**
                                  __ a fence   __ a road

4. **What does a hill look like?**   __ high land   __ low land

5. **What is a hole?**   __ an opening   __ a window

 Find two other words in the book that are about ranches. Write them in your Journal.

✔ Use for Grading

Name _____ **Date** _____

A Beautiful View

A Read the paragraph below, and find four words that look like Spanish words. Circle the words.

> *Vista* means "view." The view from my ranch is beautiful. I can see a big hill and tall trees. Outside my window there is a green cactus that looks like a fork. When the moon is bright, I might see a coyote chasing a rabbit.

B Use the circled words to answer the questions below.

1. I am a place to raise animals. What am I? _____

2. I am a beautiful view. What am I? _____

3. I am a wild animal that looks like a small dog. What am I? _____

4. I am a tall green plant. You can find me on the cover of your book. What am I? _____

Name _____ **Date** _____

Short a

The letter *a* can stand for the sound you hear in the word *hat*.

A Circle the word that names the picture. Then write the word on the line.

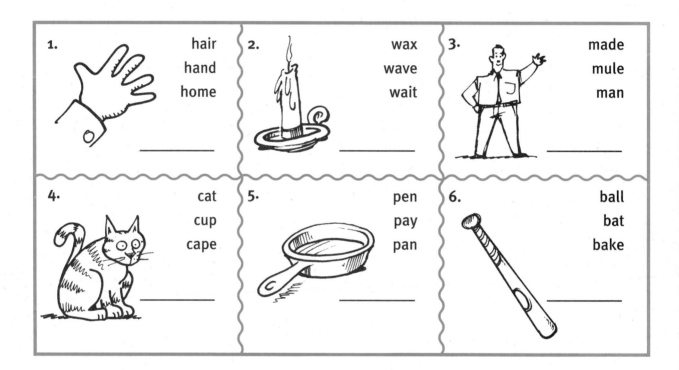

1. hair
hand
home
_____

2. wax
wave
wait
_____

3. made
mule
man
_____

4. cat
cup
cape
_____

5. pen
pay
pan
_____

6. ball
bat
bake
_____

B Replace the underlined letter in each word with an *a*. Write the new word.

1. c<u>u</u>t _____

2. m<u>e</u>n _____

3. b<u>u</u>t _____

4. r<u>o</u>t _____

5. m<u>u</u>d _____

6. h<u>i</u>s _____

 Find three more words with the short *a* sound in the book. Write them in your Journal.

✓ Use for Grading

Name _____ **Date** _____

GET READY TO WRITE!

Name of Character: me

Problem: I missed the bus. I was late!

Solution: I walked to school.

Name of Character: me

Problem: I lost my

cat in the

park.

Solution:

WANTED

LOST

Name of Character: _____

Problem: _____

Solution: _____

Name _____ **Date** _____

What's the Problem?
What's the Solution?

You've chosen your character and organized your ideas. Now it's time to write your problem and its solution.

Tips

Tell about a problem that the character has.

What happens because of the problem?

Tell how the character solves the problem.

Name _____ **Date** _____

Telling, Question, and Exclamatory Sentences

A On the first line, write the punctuation mark for each sentence. Then write *D* if it is a declarative sentence, *I* if it is an interrogative sentence, and *E* if it is an exclamatory sentence.

> ## Tip
>
> A declarative sentence tells something and ends with a period. An interrogative sentence asks something and ends with a question mark. An exclamatory sentence expresses strong feelings and ends with an exclamation mark.

1. Do you think Fox liked chickens ___ ___

2. The fox yelled, "Let me go" ___ ___

3. The fox talked to the coyote ___ ___

4. The coyote asked the fox, "What

   happened to you" ___ ___

5. The owner of the ranch made a wax man ___ ___

B Imagine that you are the owner of the ranch. Use the sentence types in parentheses ( ) to write sentences you might say to the fox.

1. (Telling) _____

   _____

2. (Question) _____

   _____

3. (Exclamatory) _____

   _____

 Write one example of each kind of sentence in your Journal.

Name _____ **Date** _____

Words With Short Vowel *a*

and
ranch
man
hand
ran
answer
wax
angry

Memory Tip
There is a wax man on the ranch.

A The letter *a* stands for the short *a* sound. Read and say the words. Write the spelling word or words from above that rhyme.

1. fan, van _____ _____

2. band, land _____ _____

3. ax, tax _____

B Complete each sentence with a spelling word from above.

1. Fox was _____ at the wax man.

2. There were chickens on the _____ .

3. The telephone is ringing. _____ it.

4. The book is in my left _____ .

5. I _____ all the way home.

✔ Use for Grading

Name _____ **Date** _____

Consonant Clusters sm- and st-

The letters *sm* stand for the sounds you hear at the beginning of *smile*. The letters *st* stand for the sounds you hear at the beginning of *stairs*.

A Read the words below. Circle the consonant clusters that make the *sm* sounds in *smile*. Underline the consonant clusters that make the *st* sounds in *stairs*.

start   smart   stars

smell   steam

B Read each sentence. Complete the sentence with a consonant cluster from above.

1. I love the _____ of cookies baking in the oven!

2. Nina is very _____. She answered all the questions correctly.

3. At night, I can see the moon and the _____ in the sky.

4. What time does the movie _____?

5. When water boils, it turns to _____.

Find three more words with the consonant clusters *sm-* and *st-*. Write them in your Journal.

Name _____ **Date** _____

Each Day / One Day

Each day tells you about something you do every day. *One day* tells you about something you would like to do sometime in the future.

Fill in the blank in each sentence with either *each day* or *one day*.

1.

_____ I will travel all over the world.

2.

I eat breakfast _____ .

3.

_____ I will drive a car.

4. What would you like to do *one day*?

_____

Think of two other things that you would like to do one day, and write a sentence about each in your Journal.

Name _____ **Date** _____

Reflect and Respond

A Read each question. Then fill in the bubble next to the best answer.

1. What was the problem on the ranch?

○ **a.** The coyote stole chickens.

○ **b.** The fox stole chickens.

○ **c.** The wax man stole chickens.

2. What did the owner of the ranch do?

○ **a.** He bought a dog to scare away the fox.

○ **b.** He hid all the chickens.

○ **c.** He made a wax man to scare away the fox.

3. How did the fox get stuck to the wax man?

○ **a.** She hit and kicked the man.

○ **b.** She ran away from the man.

○ **c.** She talked to the man.

B Read the questions. Write your answers on the lines.

1. How does Fox get free from the wax man?

_____

_____

2. How does Coyote get free from the wax man?

_____

_____

What Do You Think? Do you think Fox will ever steal chickens again? Why or why not?

Name _____ **Date** _____

Amazing Animals

Story Words

tallest having the greatest height compared to two or more other things

smallest having the least size compared to two or more other things

slowest to move with the least amount of speed compared to two or more other things

faster to move more quickly than someone or something else

feet a measurement of the length or height of someone or thing

Everyday Words

best superior to all others

move to change position or place

animal a living thing that can breath and move

across from one side to the other

longer of greater length than someone or something else

A Use the Story Words to complete the chart below. Write the words that measure size, height, speed, and length in the correct box.

Size	Height	Speed	Length

B Write the Everyday Word that completes the sentences below.

1. He is the _____ runner on the team.

2. The elephant is the biggest land _____.

3. Please _____ the chair to the table.

4. The snail moved _____ the street.

5. Pedro's foot is _____ than mine.

 Find three other words in the book that tell about height, speed, or length. Write the words in your Journal.

✔ Use for Grading

Name _____   **Date** _____

The Giraffe and the Eel

A Read the sentences below, and find five words that look like Spanish words. Underline those words.

flexible

volts

animal

electric

giraffe

1. The giraffe is the animal with the longest neck.

2. Its neck is flexible so that it can reach tall leaves and drink water from the ground.

3. The electric eel has a long body.

4. It can give a shock of up to 650 volts.

B Write the words you have underlined next to the correct definition below.

1. a living thing that can breath and move   _____

2. to be able to move in many directions   _____

3. the animal with the longest neck   _____

4. operated by electricity   _____

5. measurement of electric force   _____

Partners Look through *Biggest, Strongest, Fastest* to find other words that look like Spanish words. Share them with classmates.

Name _____ **Date** _____

The Sound of Short *i* as in the Word pin

Name each picture, and write the word on the line. Put a ✔ after the words with a short *i* sound. Circle the letters that make the short *i* sound.

1.

_____

2.

_____

3.

_____

4.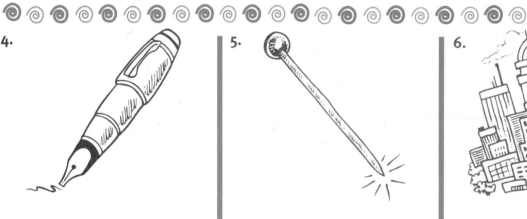

_____

5.

_____

6.

_____

7.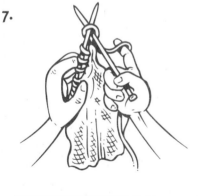

_____

8.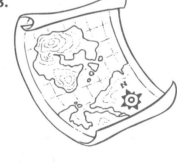

_____

9.

_____

✔ Use for Grading

Name _____   **Date** _____

GET READY TO WRITE!

Get ready to plan your sentences that give information about a sport you play or enjoy watching. Use the chart below to brainstorm ideas.

Remember

Sentences that give information contain facts, not opinions.

Name of Sport: _____

Where Played	How Many People Needed to Play	What Equipment Is Needed	How Points Are Scored

Name _____ **Date** _____

Write Informative Sentences

You have picked a favorite sport and gathered facts about the game. Now it is time to write informative sentences about it.

Tips

- Pick your sport.

- Tell where it is played.

- Tell what equipment is needed.

- Tell how many people can play in a game.

- Use complete subjects and complete predicates.

- Check spelling, especially of words with the short *i* vowel sound.

Name _____   **Date** _____

Complete Subjects/ Complete Predicates

Read the sentences below. Underline the complete subject once and the complete predicate twice. Look at the example before you begin.

Example: <u>The world's most popular sport</u> <u>is soccer</u>.

1. Chinese is spoken by more people than any other language.

2. Mexico City is the most populous city in the world.

3. The Sahara is the largest desert in the world.

4. The highest mountain in the world is Mount Everest.

5. The world's longest river is the Nile.

6. The tallest waterfall is Angel Falls in Venezuela.

7. The largest lake in the world was misnamed the Caspian Sea.

8. Fifty percent of the earth's trees are in rain forests.

9. Brazil is the largest country in South America.

10. The first country to allow women to vote was New Zealand.

Write one or more sentences about other record holders. Underline the complete subject once and the complete predicate twice in each sentence.

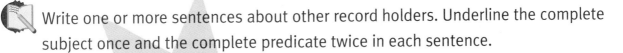

Name _____ **Date** _____

Words With Short *i*

biggest	inches	with	little
its	animal	lives	is

Memory Tip

The inchworm is
a little animal.

A Write the spelling word that completes each sentence.

1. The blue whale is the _____ water animal.

2. He _____ a kind person.

3. A baby is a _____ person.

4. I am fifty-five _____ long.

5. I like cheese sandwiches _____ tomatoes.

6. My cousin _____ in a big house.

7. The cheetah can run faster than any other _____.

8. The sun jellyfish can sting you with _____ long tentacles.

B Write the spelling words in the correct place on the chart below.

Words With One Syllable	Words With Two Syllables	Words With Three Syllables

✔ Use for Grading

Name _____ **Date** _____

Words With Initial g

The letter *g* stands for the sounds you hear in the words *girl* and *giant*. Notice that sometimes *g* has a hard sound and sometimes it has a soft sound.

A Use the words from below to complete each sentence. Then circle the letter that stands for the hard or soft *g* sound in *girl* and *giraffe*.

gem	gift	gate	gas	gentle	go

1. Be _____ with those eggs. If you drop them, they'll break.

2. Maria has a pretty white _____ in front of her house.

3. Did your friend give you a _____ for your birthday?

4. _____ away! I am trying to study for my test.

5. That ring has a sparkling green _____ in it.

6. A car needs _____ to move.

B Say the following words softly to yourself. If you hear a hard *g* sound as in *girl*, write an X under HARD. If you hear a soft *g* sound as in *giraffe*, write an X under SOFT.

	Hard	Soft
1. gift		
2. gentle		
3. go		
4. game		
5. group		
6. gem		

Partners Ask a friend to help you find two words with the soft *g* sound and two words with the hard *g* sound in the book.

✔ Use for Grading

Name _____ **Date** _____

Using Comparisons

| bigger | shorter | smaller | harder | taller | softer |

A Comparisons can be useful in describing people, places, and things. In the sentences below, you are going to describe a telephone. Choose a word from above that completes each comparison. More than one word may fit.

1. It's _____ than a pencil.

2. It's _____ than a chalk-board.

3. It's _____ than a pillow.

B Write two more sentences making up your own comparisons to describe a telephone. Think of two other objects to compare it to. You may use comparing words from above or any other comparing words you like.

4. It's _____ than a _____ .

5. It's _____ than a _____ .

Name _____   **Date** _____

Reflect and Respond

A Read each question. Fill in the bubble next to the best answer.

1. What do the illustrations in the story show you?

○ a. the sizes and shapes of animals

○ b. the oldest elephant in the world

○ c. the best way to feed baby cheetahs

2. Which animal is the strongest for its size?

○ a. cheetah

○ b. ant

○ c. sun jellyfish

3. Which animal is even bigger than the biggest dinosaur?

○ a. elephant

○ b. tortoise

○ c. blue whale

B Read each question. Answer the questions on the lines below.

1. Name three things a giraffe eats.

_____

_____

2. Where does the best animal jumper live?

_____

_____

 What Do You Think? If the elephant and the flea could talk, what might they say to one another? Write their conversation in your Journal.

✔ Use for Grading

Name _____ Date _____

Family Life

Story Words

Mom mother

Dad father

child young girl or boy

sister girl who has the same parents as another girl

adopt to take by choice into one's family

Everyday Words

morning time between sunrise and noon

name what someone is called

home where someone lives

evening between late afternoon and early night

stamped banged one's foot down

A Draw a line from the word to its meaning.

evening   banged one's foot down

Dad   after late afternoon

child   take into a family

stamped   mother

adopt   boy or girl

Mom   father

B On each line, write the correct word from the boxes.

1. Hello! My name is Ana. What's your _____ ?

2. My brother is Carlos. My _____ is Maria.

3. My house is on Water Street. Where is your _____ ?

4. I walk to school every _____ , but I take the bus home in the evening.

 Find three words in the story that name things in a home. Write them in your Journal.

✔ Use for Grading

Name _____ **Date** _____

Coming Home

A Read the paragraph. Circle five words that look like Spanish words.

> Mr. and Mrs. Green went to an office. They were very
> happy. They were going to bring Jimmy home. They had a toy
> for Jimmy. It was a big, red truck.
>
> "Thanks!" said Jimmy. "Trucks are my favorite toys!"
>
> Mrs. Green swung Jimmy and the red truck up into the air.
> "Today is a very special day. It's like a holiday!" she said.
>
> "That's right," said Mr. Green. "It's Adoption Day."

B Write each word you circled on the correct line.

1. Mr. James has a very _____ job.

2. He works in an _____ .

3. It is an _____ office.

4. We need the _____ to live.

5. It's the child's _____ story.

Name _____ **Date** _____

Long a (a-e, ay, ai)

The letters *a-e*, *ay,* and *ai* spell the long *a* sound. Sometimes you hear long *a* in the middle of a word, as in *game* or *paid*. Sometimes you hear long *a* at the end of a word, as in *day*.

A Read and say each word. Do you hear long *a*? Circle the words that have long *a* in the middle. Put an X on the words that have long *a* at the end.

name	play	go	plane	wait
see	cake	say	fly	gray

B Read and say the words. Then write a word from the box that rhymes with them.

face	may	name	raid	today

1. way, day, _____

2. same, came, _____

3. paid, maid, _____

4. race, place, _____

5. away, okay, _____

C Finish each poem. Write the word that makes a rhyme.

1. It is a very sunny day.

   I can go outside to _____ .

2. Jim and Judy like to bake.

   They made me a birthday _____ .

3. Liz said, "Hi, what's your name?

   Do you want to play a _____ ?"

cake

play

game

 Find words with the long *a* sound in *When Will We Be Sisters?* Write them in your Journal.

✔ Use for Grading

Name _____   **Date** _____

GET READY TO WRITE!

Remember

A dialogue is a conversation, or talk, between characters in a story. Dialogue shows how the characters think and feel. The characters talk like real people do.

Draw in the faces of the characters below. Write their names. In the speech balloons, write the first two things they will say.

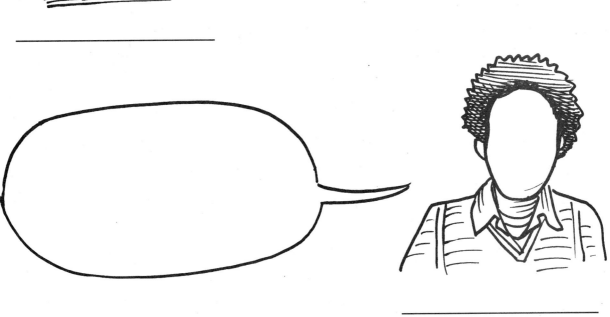

Name _____ **Date** _____

Write a Dialogue

You have chosen characters and decided what they are talking about. Now you are ready to write a dialogue. Remember to make your characters talk like real people.

Tips

Write the words that each character says.

Show what each character thinks or wants.

Use quotation marks; for example, *Patty said, "Let's go to the movies."*

Include common and proper nouns.

_____

_____

_____

_____

_____

_____

_____

_____

_____

Name _____ **Date** _____

Common and Proper Nouns

A Play Tic-Tac-Toe. To win the game, find three proper nouns in a line. They can go across, down, or from corner to corner.
Put an X on each one.

house	Sunday	Paula
ball	California	woman
Carlos	lion	Dr. Robbins

Tip

Common nouns like *teacher, home,* and *day* name any person, place, or thing. Proper nouns like *Mr. Garcia, United States,* and *Thursday* name specific people, places, and things. Proper nouns always begin with a capital letter.

B Some of the words in the puzzle pieces are proper nouns. Some are common nouns. Find the two pieces that go together. Write them.

book Cinderella month country Mexico
George Washington teacher man Ms. Frizzle July

Proper nouns   Common nouns

1. _____ is a _____

2. _____ is a _____

3. _____ is a _____

4. _____ is a _____

5. _____ is a _____

Find three proper nouns and three common nouns in the story.
Write them in your Journal.

✔ Use for Grading

Name _____ **Date** _____

Words With Long *a* Spelled *a-e, ay,* and *ai*

name	make	bake	came	
say	today	train	rain	

Memory Tip

S**ay** your n**a**m**e** as you get on the tr**ai**n.

A Play the game! May Elaine and Dave like to use words with long *a*. May Elaine likes words with *ay* and *ai*. Dave likes words with *a-e*. Write the spelling words that each one uses.

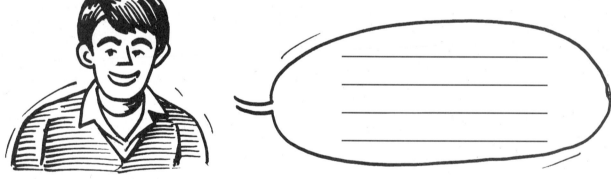

B Dave and May Elaine like to talk in rhyme, too. Finish what they say. Use words from the top of the page.

May Elaine says:

I'm calling to _____

It's my birthday _____.

Please come to my party by bus or by _____.

We'll have a picnic if it doesn't _____!

Dave says:

A present I'll _____,

And a cake I will _____.

On it I'll write your _____.

I'll be so happy I _____!

✔ Use for Grading

Name _____   Date _____

r-Controlled Vowels er, ir, ur

The letters *er, ir,* and *ur* can stand for the *r*-controlled sound you hear in *sister, dirt,* and *turn*.

A Use the words from below to complete each sentence. Then circle the letters that stand for the controlled *r* sound in each word.

burn	over	after	first	hurt	fur

1. Ouch! I _____ my leg today when I was playing soccer.

2. Be careful not to get too close to the hot stove. You might _____ yourself.

3. _____ I have breakfast. Then I get dressed.

4. Linda's kitten has gray and white _____ .

5. Do you watch television _____ you do your homework?

6. Look _____ there!

B Say the following words aloud. Listen for the controlled *r* sound as in *sister, dirt,* and *turn*. If you hear the sound, write an X under Yes. If you do not hear the sound, write an X under No.

	YES	NO			YES	NO
1. curl	____	____		4. brother	____	____
2. corn	____	____		5. roll	____	____
3. turtle	____	____		6. circle	____	____

 Look for more words in the book with the controlled *r* sound. Write them in your Journal.

Name _____   Date _____

It's Your Turn

There are many different expressions that have the word *turn* in them. In the book you read, Mom and Dad *took turns* speaking on the telephone. Lisa and Paula argued about *whose turn it was* to set the table.

 A   Finish what each person says. Use the word *turn*.

B   Read each question. Write your answer on the line. Be sure to use an expression with *turn*.

What do you say . . .

1. when you want the TV off?

_____

2. when you want someone to look behind him or her?

_____

3. when you want the driver of a car to go left?

_____

4. when you are playing a game and it's your chance?

_____

5. when you want your reading partner to go on in the book?

_____

Name _____ **Date** _____

Reflect and Respond

A Read each question. Fill in the bubble next to the best answer.

1. What is one way you can tell this book is realistic fiction?

○ **a.** It tells about events that could never happen in real life.

○ **b.** The people use everyday language when they talk.

○ **c.** The story takes place on the planet Mars.

2. What news about the adoption makes Paula very happy?

○ **a.** She finds out that the child is a girl.

○ **b.** The child will move in right away.

○ **c.** She can go to the adoption office.

3. Why do the girls argue?

○ **a.** They each want to go to bed at a different time.

○ **b.** They don't agree about whose turn it is to set the table.

○ **c.** Lisa's rag doll, Pilar, is torn.

B Read the questions. Write your answers on the lines.

1. Why do Paula and Mom clean out dresser drawers?

_____

2. How do Paula and Lisa feel about each other at the end of the story?

_____

What Do You Think? The family changes from the beginning of the story until its end. In what main way is it different?

✔ Use for Grading

Name _____ Date _____

Folktale Words

Story Words	Everyday Words
fisherman a man whose job is to catch fish	**wife** a woman who is married
magic power to make impossible things happen	**fish** an animal that has gills and lives in lakes or oceans
pull opposite of *push*	**water** the liquid that falls as rain and is found in lakes and oceans
wish a strong desire or longing for something	**sea** the ocean
prince the son of a king and queen	**happy** feeling good; pleased and contented

Use the words in the boxes to finish each sentence. Write the words on the lines.

1. I had to _____ hard to open the door.

2. I drank a glass of _____.

3. The queen's son is the _____.

4. I got wet when I fell in the _____.

5. That woman is his _____.

6. The story told about a _____ lamp.

7. Seeing my friends makes me _____.

8. She wants to eat a _____.

9. The girl got her _____ when she made the team.

10. The _____ rides to work in a boat.

 Find three more folktale words in the book. Write them in your Journal.

✔ Use for Grading

Name _____   Date _____

Make Connections!

| magic | potatoes | boots | flowers |

A Think of a Spanish word that describes each picture below. Then find a similar English word in the box. Write the English word on the line.

1.

_____

2.

_____

3.

_____

4.

_____

B Use words from the box to solve each riddle below.

1. It is something to eat. _____

2. You can wear them. _____

3. It happens in folktales. _____

4. They're colorful and make a great present. _____

Partners Make up your own riddles for each of the four words.

Name _____ **Date** _____

sh and th

The letters *sh* stand for the sound you hear at the beginning of *she* and at the end of *fish*. The letters *th* can stand for the sound you hear at the beginning of *this*.

A Read the words below. Circle each word that has the same sound that you hear at the end of *fish*. Underline each word that has the same sound you hear at the beginning of *the*.

wish	was	that	shall
asked	fisherman	dish	there

B Read each sentence. Fill in each blank with one of the words above.

1. You put food on a _____ .

2. If you are not here, you are _____ .

3. *Cat* rhymes with the word _____ .

4. Close your eyes and make a _____ .

5. The man in the boat is a _____ .

✔ Use for Grading

Name ——————————————— **Date** ———————————

GET READY TO WRITE!

Remember
In a folktale a character may make a magic wish. What will happen when the new character meets the magic fish?

Make up a character to write about. Give the character a name.	———————————————
In the space, draw a picture or use words to tell what your character looks like.	
How does your character meet the magic fish?	
What wish does your character ask the fish for?	
What happens after your character makes the wish?	

Name _____   **Date** _____

Write a Story Innovation

You have a character. You know what you want to happen in the story. Now it is time to put your ideas in sentence form and write your story.

Tips

Use details.

Tell about your character.

Tell how he or she meets the fish and gets a wish.

Tell what the wish is and what happens because of it.

Once upon a time _____

_____

_____

_____

_____

_____

_____

_____

_____

_____

Name _____ **Date** _____

Action Verbs

A Read each sentence and the words below it.
Circle the action verb that completes
each sentence.

1. Ana _____ her new bike.

   rides   happy   girl

2. The dog _____ with the ball.

   friend   silly   played

3. The woman _____ a story about a magic fish.

   home   writes   funny

B Underline the action verb in each sentence.
Sample: The woman <u>ran</u> down the hill.

1. The man sits in the boat.

2. The fish swims fast.

3. The woman thinks of a new house.

4. The fish talks to the man.

5. The man asks the fish for a wish.

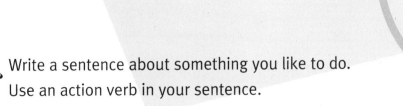

Write a sentence about something you like to do.
Use an action verb in your sentence.

Name _____   **Date** _____

Imagine that you are in Antarctica. You want to send a postcard to a friend. How will you describe Antarctica? Write your ideas on the chart.

Remember

A description tells many details about a place. Vivid nouns, adjectives, and verbs will help the reader picture the place.

1. What can you see in Antarctica?

_____

_____

_____

2. What can you hear in Antarctica?

_____

_____

_____

3. What are some adjectives that describe Antarctica?

_____

_____

_____

4. How does Antarctica make you feel?

_____

_____

_____

Copyright © Scholastic Inc.

Name _____ **Date** _____

Write a Postcard

You have organized your ideas about Antarctica. Now you can write a postcard about it. Try to paint a picture with words.

Tips

Use details to help the reader picture and "hear" Antarctica.

Put together the facts about how it looks. Do the same with the facts about what you hear.

Use vivid adjectives.

Write whole sentences.

Name _____   **Date** _____

Pronouns

A Read the fable "The Lion and the Mouse." Some of the pronouns are missing from the story. Write a pronoun from below in each blank to finish the story.

he	me	his
I	her	she
you	they	them

Tip

A pronoun is a word that can take the place of a noun. *I, she, we, him, our,* and *their* are examples of pronouns.

The Lion and the Mouse

A lion was sleeping. Suddenly, a mouse ran across _____ face. The lion woke up. He was very angry. "I'm going to eat you!" _____ roared.

The little mouse trembled. "Please don't eat me," she said. "Some day _____ will find a way to help you."

"Ha, ha!" laughed the lion. "How can a weak little animal like you help a brave, strong animal like _____ ?" But the lion let _____ go.

One day the lion was caught in a net made of rope. All the animals heard him roar. They didn't help him because _____ were too afraid. The mouse ran to the lion. "I will help you," _____ said. The mouse began to chew on the ropes. Soon she was able to cut _____ with her sharp teeth.

"Thank _____ , little mouse" said the lion. "Now I know that the weak can help the strong."

B Write two sentences. Use the pronoun *my* in one sentence. Use *we* in the other. If the pronoun is the first word in the sentence, use a capital letter.

1. _____

2. _____

 Find five pronouns in the book you read. Write them in your Journal.

Name _____ **Date** _____

Words With Short *e*

eggs	men	nests	pebbles
penguin	tell	when	yet

A The letter *e* stands for the short *e* sound. Say the spelling word that names each picture. Write the word.

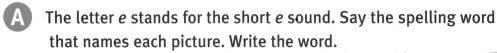

1. _____

2. _____

3. _____

4. _____

5. _____

B Read and say the words. Write the spelling word or words that rhyme.

1. well, fell, _____

2. rests, tests, _____

3. ten, hen, _____ , _____

4. pet, wet, _____

5. legs, begs, _____

C Complete each sentence with a spelling word from above.

1. A cow gives milk, and a hen lays _____.

2. Girls grow up to be women, and boys grow up to be _____.

3. Very small rocks are _____.

4. A black-and-white bird that lives in Antarctica is a _____.

5. Some birds build _____ in trees.

✔ Use for Grading

Name _____ **Date** _____

A Silent c

At the end of a word, the letters *ck* stand for the sound *k* makes.

A Say the name of each picture. Make a check (✔) in the box if you hear the sound of *k* at the end of the word. Make an X if you don't.

B Finish the funny sentences. Write the two letters that make the sound of *k* at the end of the words.

1. I carry a bla_ _ sa_ _ in the pa_ _ on my ba_ _.

2. Please be qui_ _ when you pi_ _ up the chi_ _ on the bri_ _.

3. Find the blo_ _ in the so_ _ and the ro_ _ on the clo_ _.

Write the 4 -ack words	Write the 4 -ick words.	Write the 4 -ock words.
_____	_____	_____
_____	_____	_____
_____	_____	_____
_____	_____	_____

 Use any three of the words above in a funny sentence about a giraffe.

✔ Use for Grading

Name _____ **Date** _____

Baby Animals

kid   calf   kitten   puppy

A From the words above, write the name of the baby animal under the picture of the mother.

_____ _____ _____ _____

B Finish each rhyme with the name of the baby animal. Write one of the words from above.

1. The farmer's wife began to laugh

   When she saw the cow and its baby _____ .

2. Do you know the poem about a lost mitten

   And a mother cat and her sad, little _____ ?

3. In the barn lives a horse called Sid,

   Two cats, a mouse, a goat, and a _____ .

4. Here's a picture of Tom and me

   And our big, brown dog and its new _____ .

C Challenge yourself! Different animals may have baby animals with the very same name. What are they?

1. A baby penguin is called a chick. What other animal baby is a chick? _____

2. Several animals have cubs. What are two of them? _____ and _____

 Find the words that name baby animals in *Antarctica*. Write them.

Name _____   **Date** _____

Reflect and Respond

A Read each question. Fill in the bubble in front of the correct answer.

1. Why do the emperor penguins have to feed at sea?

○ **a.** They cannot fly.

○ **b.** They eat fish.

○ **c.** It is too cold to stay on land.

2. Which words best describe Antarctica?

○ **a.** rainy and cold

○ **b.** dark and wooded

○ **c.** icy and cold

3. What may be the new enemies of the animals in Antarctica?

○ **a.** leopard seals   ○ **b.** people   ○ **c.** skuas

4. What does *pup* mean in this sentence? *"A Weddell seal climbs onto the ice to have her pup."*

○ **a.** a baby dog   ○ **b.** a baby penguin   ○ **c** a baby seal

B What is the order of the events in the story? Write 1 in front of what happens first, 2 in front of what happens next, and so on.

_____ The male emperor penguin goes to sea to feed.

_____ The Adélie penguins lay their eggs.

_____ The female emperor penguin lays her egg.

_____ The emperor chick hatches.

What Do You Think? What will happen to the animals in the years to come?

✔ Use for Grading

Name _____ **Date** _____

Words About Fun

Story Words

slide a smooth, slanted surface that children play on

swings play equipment that you sit on and move forward and backward

sandbox box filled with sand

merry-go-round play equipment that moves in circles

piano a musical instrument with a keyboard

Everyday Words

park an area with grass and trees where people play and relax

fun a good time

fair an outdoor event with rides, entertainment, and food

pictures images like photographs

dance to move with music

 A Draw a line from the word on the left to its definition on the right.

1. piano	**a.** to move with music
2. merry-go-round	**b.** a musical instrument played with the fingers
3. dance	**c.** a place where people go to play and relax
4. slide	**d.** play equipment that moves in circles
5. park	**e.** a slanted surface that children play on

 B Complete each word with the correct letter to get a vocabulary word from the boxes.

1. _ un   **3.** sw _ ngs

2. s _ ndbox   **4.** pictu _ es

5. dan _ e   **6.** sl _ de

 Find three other words in *Fox in Love* that tell about having fun. Write them in your Journal.

✔ Use for Grading

Name _____   **Date** _____

Similar Words

| park | idea | piano | music | camera |

A Name each picture below. Then, from the words above, write the word on the line.

1. _____

2. _____

3. _____

4. _____

5. _____

B Write the words from above next to the correct definitions below.

1. something used to take pictures _____

2. a place to play and relax _____

3. a musical instrument _____

4. a thought or a plan _____

5. an arrangement of sounds that go together _____

Partners Find three other words in *Fox in Love* that are similar to Spanish words.
Share them with a partner.

Name _____ **Date** _____

Short o

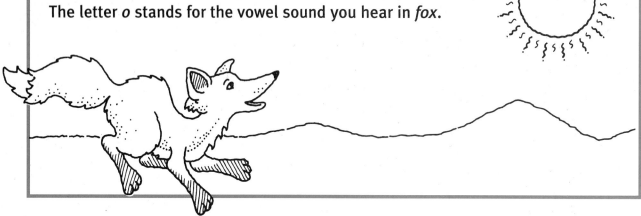

The letter *o* stands for the vowel sound you hear in *fox*.

A Read the words below. Circle each word that has the same vowel sound as *fox*.

run	luck	rock	sock
stop	mud	sandbox	bus

B Read each sentence. Fill in the blank with one of the words you circled above. Each word you choose should have the same vowel sound as *fox*.

1. I can't put on my shoe because I can't find my _____.

2. Playing in the _____ is my favorite activity at the park.

3. Oh no! I think the bus driver missed my bus _____.

4. The lizard is sitting on a _____ in the sun.

 As you read the book, find two other words with short *o*.
Write them in your Journal.

✔ Use for Grading

Name _____ **Date** _____

GET READY TO WRITE!

**Remember**

A persuasive dialogue should make a person do something or go somewhere.

Why is the park a great place to spend the day?
Use the chart to help organize your thoughts.

What kinds of games and activities can you play or do at the park?	What is the weather like outside?	Who is at the park?
_____	_____	_____
_____	_____	_____
_____	_____	_____
_____	_____	_____
_____	_____	_____
_____	_____	_____
_____	_____	_____

Name _____ **Date** _____

Write a Dialogue

You've made a list of reasons why the park is a great place to spend the day, and you've organized your thoughts. Now it's time to write your persuasive dialogue.

Tips

Write as if you're *talking* to your friend.

Use words like *let's go*, *come on*, and *please*.

Make the park sound like a place to have fun.

Use plural nouns.

Name _____ **Date** _____

Plural Nouns

A Read each sentence and the words below it.
Circle the word that completes each sentence correctly.

1. I borrowed some _____ from the library.

bookes   book   books

2. I saw three brown _____ in the field.

foxs   fox   foxes

3. It was so cold outside that Marco wore three _____!

sweaters   sweateres   sweater

4. I have many interesting _____.

friend   friends   friendes

5. Dolores rides two different _____ to school every day.

bus   buses   buss

B Write three sentences using number words and plural nouns of your choice. Underline the number words and circle the plural nouns in each sentence.

1. _____

_____

2. _____

_____

3. _____

_____

 Write two sentences about Fox in your Journal.
Use one plural noun in each sentence.

Name _____ **Date** _____

Words With Short *o*

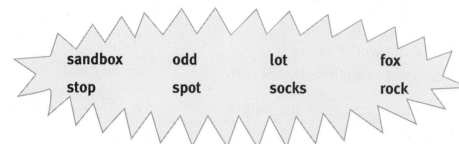

sandbox   odd   lot   fox

stop   spot   socks   rock

Memory Tip

There is an **odd** spot
on F**o**x's s**o**cks.

A Each word above has a short *o* sound. Sort the spelling words in alphabetical order. You will have to look at the *second* letter in four of the words.

1. _____
2. _____
3. _____
4. _____

5. _____
6. _____
7. _____
8. _____

B Write the spelling word that names each picture. Then circle the letter that makes the short *o* sound in each word.

1. _____

2. _____

3. _____

4. _____

✔ Use for Grading

Name _____ **Date** _____

Short u

The letter *u* can stand for the vowel sound in *up*.

A Say the name of each pair of pictures. Circle the one that has the vowel sound in *up*.

B Write the word that goes with each pair.

jump

bus

under

drum

skunk

1. horn, piano, _____

2. truck, van, _____

3. rabbit, deer, _____

4. hop, skip, _____

5. over, behind, _____

C Answer each riddle with two words that rhyme. Use the words in the box. The first one is done for you.

lucky	bug	cub	ducky	pup	tub	rug	cup

1. What's a race in the sunshine?   a __sun__ __run__

2. What does a puppy like to drink from?   a _____ _____

3. What's a mat that ladybugs like to sit in?   a _____ _____

4. What do baby bears take a bath in?   a _____ _____

5. What's a duck that won a contest?   a _____ _____

 Look in the story for five other words with the short *u* sound. Write them in your Journal.

✔ Use for Grading

Name _____ **Date** _____

Words With Multiple Meaning

Many words have more than one meaning. We use the words and phrases surrounding a multiple-meaning word to identify its definition.

| watch | turn | park | left | right |

A Unscramble the words below, and write them on the line. Use the words above as a guide.

1. tawch _____

2. tefl _____

3. nurt _____

4. kpra _____

5. trigh _____

tawch

B Solve the riddles with a word from above.

1. It has a face and two hands, and it tells you the time.

_____

2. You visit it when you want to run and play with your friends.

_____

3. This is a direction, opposite from left.

_____

Write two sentences in your Journal. Use the word *turn* in one sentence and *left* in the other. Then share your sentences with a partner. Can your partner tell you the meaning of *turn* and *left* in your sentences?

Name _____ **Date** _____

Reflect and Respond

A Read each question. Circle the bubble in front of the best answer.

1. What did Raisin do when the pictures fell out of Fox's pocket?

○ **a.** She smiled at Fox.

○ **b.** She became angry and walked away from Fox.

○ **c.** She became ill with the mumps.

2. How did Fox solve his problem when Raisin got the mumps?

○ **a.** He went to the park with other friends.

○ **b.** He took his sister to the dance.

○ **c.** He stayed home and watched TV.

3. What happened at the dance contest?

○ **a.** Fox and Louise won first prize.

○ **b.** Fox and Raisin won second prize.

○ **c.** Fox and Louise won second prize.

B Read the questions. Write your answers on the lines.

1. Where did Fox get his pictures taken with the three pretty foxes?

_____

2. What happened when Fox went to Raisin's house the day of the Big Dance Contest?

_____

_____

What Do You Think? Do you think Fox and Raisin will still be friends after the Big Dance Contest? Explain your answer.

✔ Use for Grading

Name _____   Date _____

Baseball Words

Story Words	**Everyday Words**
tryouts a test of an athlete's abilities	**decided** made up one's mind
baseball a game played with a hard ball and a bat by two teams of nine players each	**anyone** any one person in a group
shortstop position between second and third	**player(s)** a person who takes part in a game
scout person who spots athletes	**sport(s)** a game or contest
practice to do over and over to gain greater skill	**team** a group of people who work together

A Words made up of two smaller words are called compounds: *basket + ball = basketball*. Draw a line between bats and balls to make compounds. Write the words.

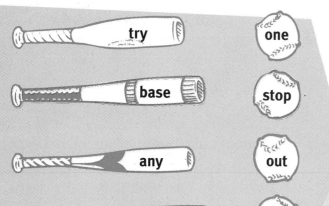

try   one   1. _____

base   stop   2. _____

any   out   3. _____

short   ball   4. _____

B Solve the riddles. Write a word from the box on each line.

1. It can be soccer, baseball, or swimming. What is it? _____

2. They are the people who play a game. Who are they? _____

3. It's a group of people that plays together. What is it? _____

4. It's what you must do to become very skilled. What is it? _____

5. It's the person who looks for good players to hire. Who is it? _____

6. It's what you did when you made up your mind. What is it? _____

✔ Use for Grading

Name _____ **Date** _____

Who Was He?

A Read the paragraph about a famous baseball player who lived many years ago.
Find five words that look like Spanish words and circle them.

> Babe Ruth was one of baseball's greatest players. One year he hit 29 doubles, 8 triples, and 60 home runs! He was voted into the Baseball Hall of Fame. Here's a story about him.
>
> It was September 1932. Ruth's team, the New York Yankees, was playing against the Chicago Cubs in the World Series. The Chicago fans booed Ruth. He decided, "I'll show them!" When he went up to bat, he pointed to the seats that were farthest away. The fans just laughed. The pitcher threw the ball. The great Ruth hit it. The ball went just where he had pointed. It was a home run!

B Draw a line from each word to its meaning.

voted   hits that allow the player to get to third base

doubles   made up one's mind

September   hits that allow the player to get to second base

decided   chose in an election

triples   the ninth month of the year

Partners Find five other words in _Roberto Clemente_ that look like Spanish words.
Share them with a partner.

Name _____ **Date** _____

Long e Spelled ea

A Say the word that names each picture. Listen to the vowel sound. If it is the long *e* sound, circle Yes. If it is not long *e*, circle No.

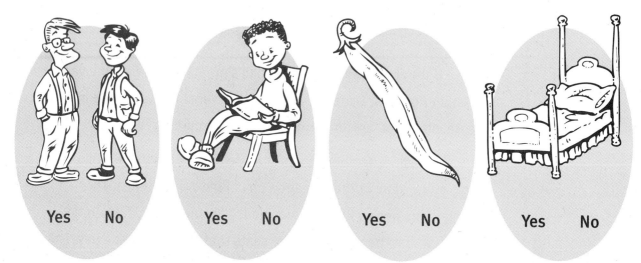

Yes   No   Yes   No   Yes   No   Yes   No

B Read the first word. Change the *e* to make a new word with long *e* spelled *ea*.

net   n__ __t

met   m__ __t

red   r__ __d

men   m__ __n

Read the sentences. Fill in the blanks. Use the words you made above.

1. Mike cleaned his room. Now it is very _____.

2. I have many books to _____.

3. The dictionary tells us what words _____.

4. For dinner, we had _____, rice, and vegetables.

 Find three words in the book that have the long *e* sound spelled *ea*. Write the words in your Journal.

✔ Use for Grading

Name _____   **Date** _____

GET READY TO WRITE!

- Whom will you write about—a friend? a teacher?

- What's your main idea? Think about what is special about the person. Is he or she a great dancer? smart? a good talker?

- What details or examples will you give to the reader? Use the chart to organize your ideas.

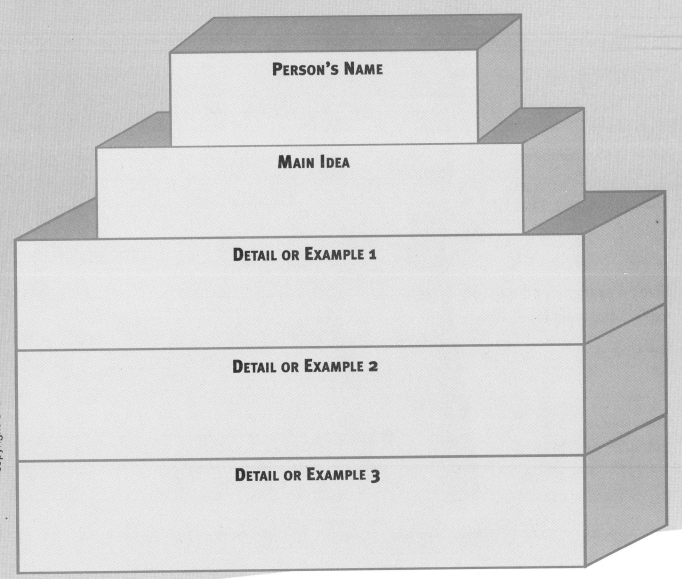

PERSON'S NAME

MAIN IDEA

DETAIL OR EXAMPLE 1

DETAIL OR EXAMPLE 2

DETAIL OR EXAMPLE 3

Name _____ **Date** _____

Write an Informative Paragraph

You are ready to write about someone you know. Look back at your plan as you write. First, write the main idea. Then, give details or examples that explain the main idea.

Tips

Whom are you
writing about?

What is special about
the person?
This will be your main idea.

Give an example or detail to
explain the main idea.

Now include other
examples or details.

_____

_____

_____

_____

_____

_____

_____

_____

_____

Name _____ **Date** _____

Subject-Verb Agreement

A Read each sentence. Circle the verb in ( ) that is correct.

1. My friend Phil (love, loves) to play baseball.

2. Phil and his friends (make, makes) their own baseballs.

3. Phil (play, plays) with real baseballs and gloves, too.

4. He (practice, practices) with a team named the Suns.

5. The owners (like, likes) him.

6. Scouts (see, sees) Phil.

7. Phil (practice, practices) every day.

8. He (become, becomes) better all the time.

9. Phil (win, wins) many games.

10. This friend (do, does) many things to help people, too.

Tip

A verb in the present tense that tells about one person, place, or thing ends in *s* or *es*. If the verb tells about more than one person, place, or thing, it does not end in *s* or *es*.

B In each sentence, which verb is correct? Write it in the blank.

1. Tim and Tina _____ different things. (like, likes)

2. Tina _____ soccer. (play, plays)

3. Her team _____ many championships. (win, wins)

4. Tim _____ computer games. (make up, makes up)

5. Their parents _____ very proud. (feel, feels)

✔ Use for Grading

Name _____ **Date** _____

Long *e* Spelled *ea, ee*

		sweet		
team	each	cheese	season	
feet	leaf		bees	

A Say the word that names the picture. Write the spelling word
or words that rhyme with it.

1.

_____

2.

_____

3.

_____

B Write the spelling word that answers each clue.

1. It grows on a tree. _____

2. It's something to eat. _____

3. They buzz around the flowers. _____

4. It's the way a peach tastes. _____

5. It rhymes with *teach*. _____

6. It means winter, spring, summer, or fall. _____

7. It's where your toes are. _____

8. It begins like *toy* and ends like *farm*. _____

 Find four other words with long *e* spelled *ea* and *ee* in *Roberto Clemente*.
Write them in your Journal.

✔ Use for Grading

Name _____ **Date** _____

The Sounds of ew and ue

Some words have the same vowel sound, but the sound can be spelled with different letters.

The letters *ue* and *ew* stand for the same vowel sound in *blue* and *flew*.

A Say the name of each picture. Draw a circle around the ones that have the sound of *ue* in *blue*.

B The vowel sounds in these words are the same. Write *ue* or *ew* to complete each word.

gl __ __   ch __ __   thr __ __

C Answer the clues. Write a word from the box on each blank.

flew	1. what you did to get taller _____
blue	2. what you did when you made a picture _____
drew	3. what you use to make things stick _____
true	4. the color of the sky and the ocean _____
threw	5. not false _____
grew	6. how a bird went away _____
glue	7. what Clemente did with a ball _____

 Find three more words with the vowel sound of *blue* spelled *ue* or *ew*. Write them in your Journal.

✔ Use for Grading

Name _____ **Date** _____

Similes

In *Roberto Clemente*, the author writes that Clemente "ran like the wind." She compares Clemente to the wind to show that he ran very fast. She also could have said, "Clemente ran as fast as the wind."

A Read each sentence. Circle the two things that are being compared. The first one is done for you.

This kind of comparison is called a simile. It says that one thing is like another. It uses the word *like* or *as*. Similes are word pictures. They make writing colorful.

1. His laugh was like thunder.

2. My hands felt like ice.

3. The cat's eyes sparkle like stars.

4. The water was like glass.

B As you read each adjective, ask yourself, "Like what?" The first one is done for you.

1. It's round like _____a ball_____ .

2. It's yellow like _____ .

3. It's as tall as _____ .

4. The cat's fur is as soft as _____ .

5. He's as smart as _____ .

C Write about something you see. Use similes to create word pictures.

1. I'm looking out the window, and I see _____ .
 (what?)

It's _____ like _____ .
 (adjective) (what?)

2. I'm looking in the classroom, and I see _____ .
 (what?)

It's as _____ as a _____ .
 (adjective) (what?)

Name _____ Date _____

Reflect and Respond

 A Read each question. Fill in the bubble in front of the correct answer.

1. Mrs. Clemente said, "Roberto was born to play baseball." What did she mean?

○ **a.** It was her dream that her son become a baseball player.

○ **b.** He was born in a baseball park.

○ **c.** Roberto was always thinking about baseball and practicing his skills.

2. Why did Mr. Clemente want Roberto to finish high school?

○ **a.** He thought education was important.

○ **b.** He did not want Roberto to become a baseball player.

○ **c.** He wanted Roberto to stay in Puerto Rico.

3. How do you know that people in baseball thought Clemente was a great player?

○ **a.** They let him play in many games.

○ **b.** They gave him many honors and awards.

○ **c.** They gave him a car.

4. Clemente wanted to build a sports center in Puerto Rico because

○ **a.** he could practice there.

○ **b.** he loved baseball.

○ **c.** girls and boys could learn to play different sports.

5. What qualities made Roberto Clemente a great man?

○ **a.** He was a very good hitter.

○ **b.** He did many things to help other people.

○ **c.** He always wanted to be a baseball player, and he became one.

Name _____

The Wax Man

Fill in the boxes. Use clues from the story and what you know.

Prediction Chart

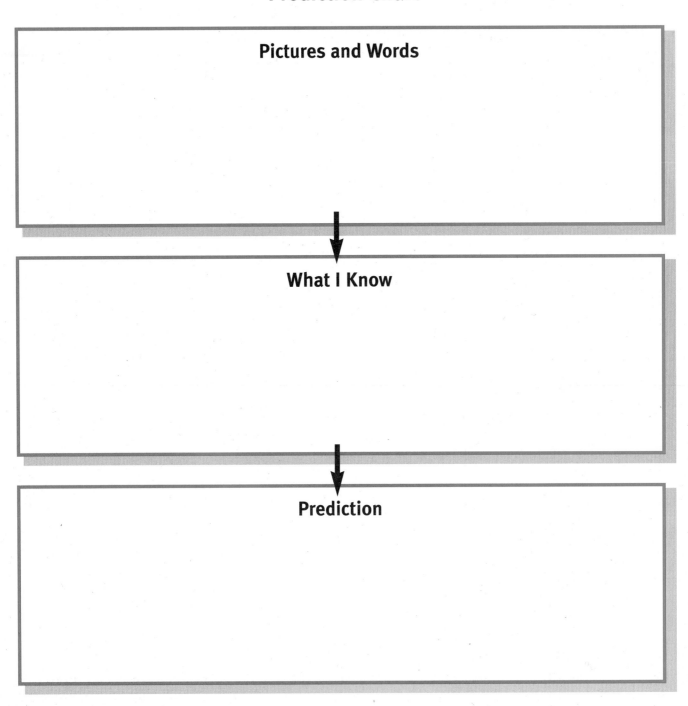

Pictures and Words

What I Know

Prediction

Name _____

READING
Independently

Biggest, Strongest, Fastest

Using clues from the pictures in *Biggest, Strongest, Fastest,* draw animals from the book in the appropriate boxes below.

Which animal is the tallest?

Which animal is the smallest bird?

Which is the biggest land animal?

Name _____

When Will We Be Sisters?

Make a story map. Fill in the boxes to tell the plot of *When Will We Be Sisters?*

Problem:

Event 1:

Event 2:

Event 3:

Event 4:

Solution:

Name ——————————————————

The Magic Fish

Fill in the empty boxes with pictures or words to tell about causes and effects in *The Magic Fish*.

Cause		Effect
	→	

Cause		Effect
	→	

Name ______________________________________

READING Independently

Ibis

Complete the chart below to show the steps taken to solve the problem in *Ibis*.

Problem	Steps to Solving the Problem	Solution

Name _____

Antarctica

Tell about the order of events in *Antarctica*. Write or draw your answers.

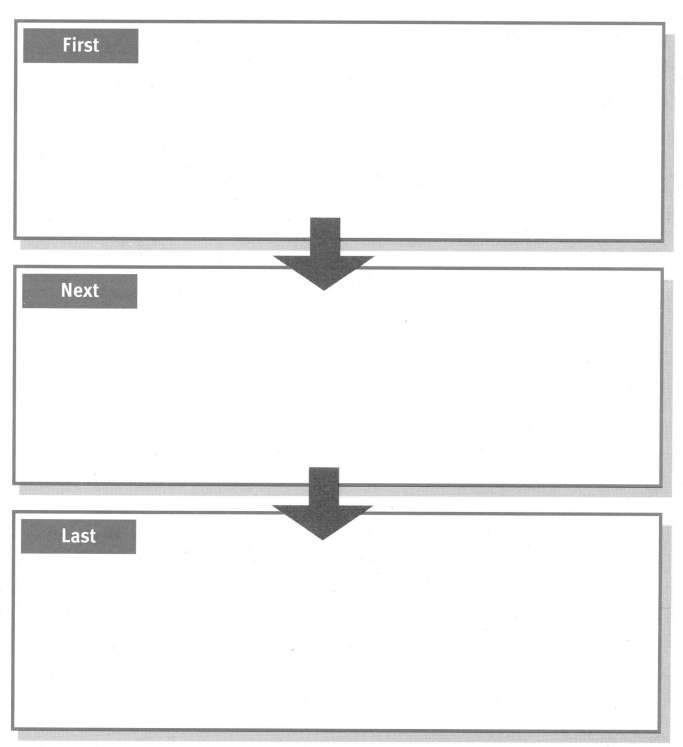

First

Next

Last

Name _____

Fox in Love

Use the Story Steps on this page to help you write a summary of *Fox in Love*.

Tell who the main character is.

Tell something important about the main character.

Tell about an important story event.

Tell what happens at the end of the story.

Name _____

Roberto Clemente: Baseball Superstar

Use the chart below to tell about the main idea and some supporting details of *Roberto Clemente: Baseball Superstar.*

Main Idea

Supporting Details

Glossary

A a

across /ə krôs/ *preposition*
From one side of to the other side of.

adopt /ə dopt/ *verb*
To take by choice, as in to *adopt* a child into one's family.

animal /an ə məl/ *noun*
A living creature that can breathe and move about.

anyone /en ē wun/ *pronoun*
Any one person in a group.

B b

baseball /bās bôl/ *noun*
A game played with a hard ball and a bat by two teams of nine players.

best /best/ *adjective or adverb*
Superior to all others.

boat /bōt/ *noun*
A vehicle used to travel on water.

C c

calf /kaf/
1. *noun* A baby whale. 2. *noun* The lower part of a person's leg.

chick(s) /chik/ *noun*
A very young chicken or other bird.

chicken /chik ən/ *noun*
A bird raised for its meat and eggs.

child /chīld/ *noun*
A young boy or girl.

coast /kōst/ *noun*
Land that is next to the sea.

coyote /kī ō tē / *noun*
An animal that looks like a small dog.

curious /kyo͞or ē əs/ *adjective*
Wanting to find out something.

D d

Dad /dad/ *noun*
Informal for *father*.

dance /dans/ *verb*
To move with music.

decided /di sī did/ *verb*
To have made up one's mind about something.

dive /dīv/ *verb*
To jump head first into water.

E e

egg /eg/ *noun*
An oval object with a covering or shell out of which young animals hatch.

evening /ēv ning/ *noun*
Time of day between late afternoon and early part of the night.

a	add	ô	order	th	this
ā	ace	o͝o	took	zh	vision
â	care	o͞o	pool		
ä	palm	u	up		
e	end	û	burn	ə	=
ē	equal	yo͞o	fuse	a	in *above*
i	it	oi	oil	e	in *sicken*
ī	ice	ou	pout	i	in *possible*
o	odd	ng	ring	o	in *melon*
ō	open	th	thin	u	in *circus*

Glossary

fair /fâr/

1. *noun* An outdoor event with rides, entertainment, and food. 2. *adjective* Good, honest, and just. 3. *adjective* Light in color.

faster /fast ər/ *adjective or adverb*

To move more quickly than someone or something else.

feet /fēt/

1. *noun* A measurement of the length or height of someone or thing. 2. *noun* Plural word for the part of the body attached to the bottom of the leg.

fence /fens/ *noun*

Something that surrounds and protects an area.

fish /fish/ *noun*

An animal that has gills and lives in lakes and oceans.

fisherman /fish ur mən/ *noun*

A man whose job is to catch fish.

fox /foks/ *noun*

A wild animal with red-brown fur.

fun /fun/ *noun or adjective*

A good time.

happy /hap ē/ *adjective*

Feeling good; pleased and contented.

hatch /hach/ *verb*

To bring forth from an egg.

hill /hil/ *noun*

An area of high land, smaller than a mountain.

hole /hōl/ *noun*

An opening in something.

home /hōm/ *noun*

Where someone lives or belongs.

hungry /hung grē/ *adjective*

Wanting food.

leave(s) /lēv/ *verb*

To go away.

longer /long gər/ *adjective*

To extend farther than someone or something else.

magic /maj ik/ *noun*

Special powers to make impossible things happen.

man /man/ *noun*

An adult male human being.

merry-go-round /mer ē gō round/ *noun*

A piece of play equipment that moves in circles.

Mom /mom/ *noun*

Informal for *mother*.

a	add	ô	order	th	this
ā	ace	ŏŏ	took	zh	vision
â	care	ōō	pool		
ä	palm	u	up		
e	end	û	burn	ə	=
ē	equal	yōō	fuse	a	in *above*
i	it	oi	oil	e	in *sicken*
ī	ice	ou	pout	i	in *possible*
o	odd	ng	ring	o	in *melon*
ō	open	th	thin	u	in *circus*

Glossary

morning /môr ning/ *noun*

Time of day between midnight and noon or sunrise and noon.

move /mo͞ov/ *verb*

To change position or place.

name /nām/ *noun*

What someone or something is called.

nest(s) /nest/ *noun*

A place built by birds and many other animals to lay their eggs and bring up their young.

net /net/ *noun*

A material made from thread; something made from this material and used to catch fish.

night /nīt/ *noun*

The time when it is dark outside.

ocean /ō shən/ *noun*

A large area of water.

park /pärk/

1. *noun* An area of land with grass and trees, used by people to play and relax in.
2. *verb* To leave a car in a space, a garage, or on the street.

penguin(s) /pen gwin/ *noun*

A water bird of the Antarctic region that cannot fly and that uses its wings as flippers for swimming.

piano /pē an ō/ *noun*

A large musical instrument with a keyboard, played with the fingers.

picture /pik chər/ *noun*

An image of something, like a photograph.

player(s) /plā ər/ *noun*

A person(s) who takes part in a game.

practice /prak tis/ *verb*

To do over and over to gain greater skill.

prince /prins/ *noun*

The son of a king and queen.

pull /po͝ol/ *verb*

The opposite of *push*.

ranch /ranch/ *noun*

A large area of land for raising animals.

Ss

sandbox /sand *boks*/ *noun*

A large wooden box that is filled with sand and used to play in.

scared /skârd/ *adjective*

Afraid.

scout /scout/ *noun*

Someone sent to locate young athletes.

a	add	ô	order	th	this
ā	ace	o͝o	took	zh	vision
â	care	o͞o	pool		
ä	palm	u	up		
e	end	û	burn	ə	=
ē	equal	yo͞o	fuse	a	in *above*
i	it	oi	oil	e	in *sicken*
ī	ice	ou	pout	i	in *possible*
o	odd	ng	ring	o	in *melon*
ō	open	th	thin	u	in *circus*

Glossary

sea /sē / *noun*

The ocean.

seal /sēl/ *noun*

A sea mammal that has thick fur and flippers.

shortstop /shôrt *stop*/ *noun*

An infielder whose position is between second and third base.

sister(s) /sis tər/ *noun*

Female who has the same parents as another person.

slide /slīd/ *noun*

A slippery, smooth surface that children play on.

slowest /slō est/ *adjective*

To move with the least amount of speed compared to two or more other things.

smallest /smôl est/ *adjective*

Having the least height compared to two or more other things.

sport /spōrt/ *noun*

A game or contest.

spring /spring/

1. *noun* The season between winter and summer, when the weather becomes warmer and flowers begin to grow.
2. *verb* To move as if bouncing.

stamped (stamp) /stampt/

1. *verb* To have banged one's foot down. 2. *noun* To have fixed a piece of paper on a piece of mail to show that you have paid to send it.

starfish /stär *fish*/ *noun*

An animal found in the ocean and shaped like a star.

swing(s) /swing/ *noun*

A piece of play equipment that you sit on and move back and forth.

tallest /tôl est/ *adjective*

Having the greatest height compared to two or more other things.

team /tēm/ *noun*

A group of people who work or play together.

tryout /trī *out*/ *noun*

A test of an athlete's abilities.

water /wôt ər/ *noun*

The liquid that falls as rain and is found in lakes and the ocean.

wax /waks/ *noun*

A material used to make candles.

whale /wāl/ *noun*

A very large sea animal.

wife /wīf/ *noun*

A woman who is married.

winter /win tər/ *noun*

The season between autumn and spring, when the weather is the coldest.

wish /wish/ *noun or verb*

A strong desire or longing for something.

a	add	ô	order	th	this
ā	ace	o͞o	took	zh	vision
â	care	o͞o	pool		
ä	palm	u	up		
e	end	û	burn		
ē	equal	yo͞o	fuse	ə	=
i	it	oi	oil	a	in *above*
ī	ice	ou	pout	e	in *sicken*
o	odd	ng	ring	i	in *possible*
ō	open	th	thin	o	in *melon*
				u	in *circus*

Spanish-English Connection (Cognates)

acrobatic/acrobático/a
adopt (to)/adoptar
*adoption/adopción
African/africano
*air/aire
algae/algas
anaconda/anaconda
*animal/animal
association/asociación
August/agosto
autograph/autografo
biography/biografía
boat/bote
*cactus/cactus
cafeteria/cafetería
*camera/cámara
capture (to)/capturar
ceremony/ceremonia
circle/círculo
*coast/costa
continent/continente
contract/contrato
*coyote/coyote
*curious/curioso/a
December/diciembre
decide (to)/decidir
destroy (to)/destruir
different/diferente
dinosaur/dinosaurio
dormitories/dormitorios
*double/doble
*electric/eléctrico/a
electricity/electricidad

elephant/elefante
exclaim/exclamar
explosion/explosión
family/familia
*favorite/favorito/a
feast/fiesta
ferocious/feroz
filaments/filamentos
*finally/finalmente
*flexible/flexible
fortunately/afortunadamente
fruit/fruta
*giraffe/girafa *or* jirafa
golf/golf
helicopter/helióptero
honor/honor
hospital/hospital
hotel/hotel
hour/hora
*idea/idea
insects/insectos
interesting/interesante
island/isla
javelin/javalina
leader/líder
*leopard/leopardo
*magic/magia
memory/memoria
microscope/microscopio
minutes/minutos
*music/música
nectar/néctar
nervous/nervioso/a
*ocean/océano

October/octubre
*office/oficina
*panic/pánico
park/parque
*part/parte
pass (to)/pasar
*penguin/pingüino
*piano/piano
pirate/pirata
plants/plantas
*potatoes/patatas
practice (to)/practicar
problem/problema
radio/radio
*ranch/rancho
real/real
*really/reaimente
record/récord
*retire (to)/retirar
rich/rico/a
*rock/roca
*September/septiembre
series/serie
*special/especial
statistics/estadística
study (to)/estudiar
tentacles/tentáculos
*terrible/terrible
trap/atrapar
*triple/triple
uniform/uniforme
version/versión
*vista/vista
*vote (to)/votar

* Cited in the Teacher's Guide.